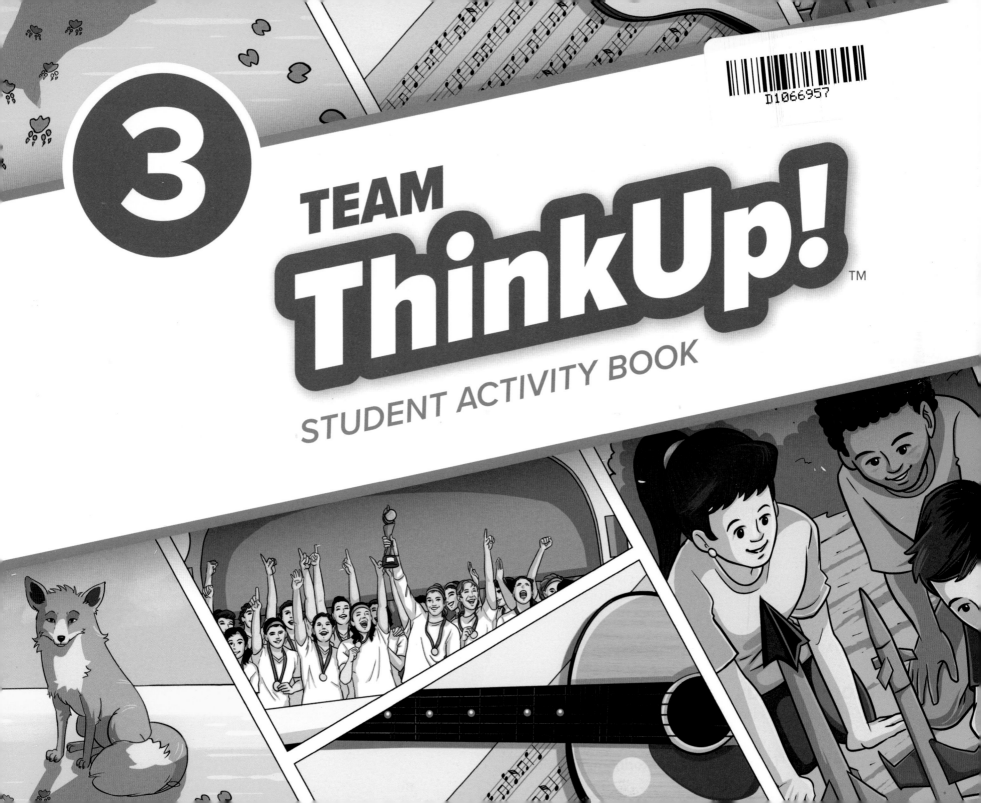

TEAM ThinkUp!™

Content Development Team

Amanda Byers
Ladona Cook
Karen Crawford

Charles Fuhrken
Karen Lane
Sandra Love

Connie Moore
Marian Rainwater
Teresa Sherman

Content Editorial Team

Anne Altamirano
Shae Connell

Digital Production Team

Nicholina Yutzy
Jonathan Puckett

Team ThinkUp! Student Activity Book

ISBN: 978-1-62763-241-6

MentoringMinds®
Critical Thinking for Life!®

800.585.5258 | **Learn more at mentoringminds.com**

Table of Contents

The Musical Toes of Tony Melendez

Tony was amazed to find himself onstage. The large audience waited excitedly to hear him sing. But they may have been more interested in watching him play his guitar. You see, Tony Melendez has no arms.

At 10 years of age, Tony told his parents that he no longer wanted to wear his prosthetic arms. He already did everything with his feet, from brushing his teeth to completing his homework. It was not surprising that Tony taught himself to play his father's guitar with his toes.

Tony had a rich voice and a talent for making music. In 1987, he performed for Pope John Paul II. The pope, an important religious leader, was seated near the stage. Tony felt nervous. He knew that millions of people were watching on television. He did not want to make a mistake.

When Tony played the last note of his song "Never Be the Same," audience members sprang from their seats to applaud. The pope rushed to the stage and embraced the young man. Tony returned the embrace with his smile and tears of joy.

The pope declared that Tony brings hope to many people with disabilities.

Adapt — I adjust my actions and strategies to accomplish tasks.

How did Tony benefit from his ability to adapt? _____

_____

_____

Record a task that you are asked to complete at school or at home.

Record the steps you follow to complete the task.

1.

2.

3.

Record one way you might adapt those steps to adjust your strategy.

Reread "The Musical Toes of Tony Melendez."

Read this sentence from the text.

> The pope declared that Tony brings hope to many people with disabilities.

What does this sentence mean?

Why does the author conclude the text with this sentence?

Write a conversation between Tony and a child who always says, "I can't!"

Tony used a new strategy to play music. Music is an example of sound energy.

Look at the materials pictured below.

Draw a picture to show how the materials might be adapted to make musical instruments.

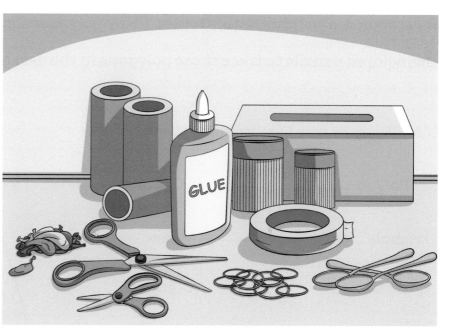

Describe two different actions you might use to explore sound energy with the instruments.

_____

_____

_____

_____

_____

_____

When you adapt, you look at things in different ways.

A decagon is a polygon with 10 sides. Many polygons can be found within this decagon.

Use colored pencils to trace these polygons in the decagon.

Hint: Polygons may have irregular shapes.

Polygon	Number of Sides	Color
triangle	3	yellow
quadrilateral	4	orange
pentagon	5	red
hexagon	6	purple
heptagon	7	blue
octagon	8	green
nonagon	9	brown
decagon	10	black

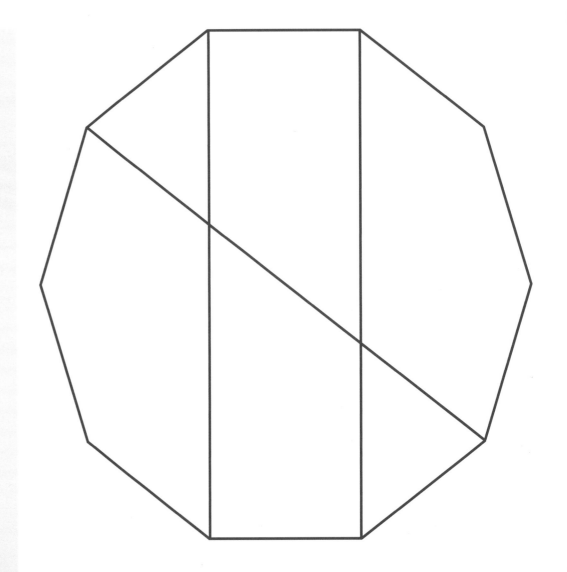

CHECK MY THINKING

A cinquain is a five-line poem that does not rhyme but follows a pattern. **Study the pattern.**

Line 1: one word topic

Line 2: two words about the topic

Line 3: three words about the topic

Line 4: four words about the topic

Line 5: one word topic

Write a cinquain showing what you have learned about the critical thinking trait *adapt*.

Line 1: **Adapt**

Line 2: _____ _____

Line 3: _____ _____ _____

Line 4: _____ _____ _____ _____

Line 5: **Adapt**

SELF-ASSESSMENT Adapt

Adapt – I adjust my actions and strategies to accomplish tasks.

Think about what you have learned about the critical thinking trait *adapt*.

Read the sentences. Color your answer.

I know when I need to try a new way to do something.

I adapt when I should.

Sometimes I adapt, but sometimes I need help.

I never adapt.

Adapt: The Musical Toes of Tony Melendez

Why Geese Fly in a V-Formation

In the fall, thousands of Canadian geese fly south. This flight helps them escape the harsh winter weather. The geese make long treks with one goose flying in the lead position. The other geese trail behind in two close lines. Why do geese choose to travel this way?

The goose that leads the flock has an important job: breaking the airflow. The geese flying behind the lead goose are given lift, or a boost. This means they use less energy to fly.

Being in the lead, though, becomes tiring for the head goose. So the lead goose drops out of the front position and rejoins the formation in a different position. Another goose then assumes the lead.

Flying in the V-formation helps the geese stay together as a group. Their flying pattern also helps them communicate. They honk and make 13 different calls, including loud greetings and alarm calls.

Geese are efficient travelers as they work together to reach warmer climates.

EXPLORE THE TRAIT:

Collaborate — I work with others to achieve better outcomes.

What lessons might people learn from the ways in which geese work together?

_____

Use pictures and words to summarize the text "Why Geese Fly in a V-Formation" in the first speech bubble. Then ask a partner to write a summary in the second speech bubble.

My Summary

My Partner's Summary

Use the information from both speech bubbles to write a collaborative summary of the text.

_____

_____

_____

Infographic is a word formed using the word part *info* for information and *graphic*. An infographic combines words and images to display facts and details about a topic.

In small groups, conduct research about geese. In the left-hand box, record notes from your research. In the right-hand box, sketch your group's design for an infographic about geese.

Notes (ideas, learnings, wonderings)	Sketch of infographic

Transfer your group's final infographic about geese to a large sheet of paper to display.

Many organisms, such as geese, work together to help them survive.

Describe how the organisms in each image benefit from working together.

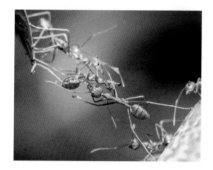

_____

_____

_____

_____

_____

_____

_____

_____

_____

Sometimes, collective nouns name animals living in groups.

Work with a partner to match the animals to their group names. Use reference materials as needed.

birds   colony

fish   crash

lions   flock

lizards   lounge

porcupines   pack

prairie dogs   prickle

rhinoceroses   pride

wolves   school

When you collaborate, you work with others to find a solution to a problem.

Work in groups of three to find the solution to this question.

A farmer bought a goose for $10 and then sold it for $15.

He bought the goose again for $20 and sold it again for $25.

What is the result of these transactions?

Check one of the possible results.

☐ The farmer lost $5.

☐ The farmer lost $10.

☐ The farmer lost $15.

☐ The farmer neither lost nor earned money.

☐ The farmer earned $5.

☐ The farmer earned $10.

☐ The farmer earned $15.

☐ Other _____

Justify your response.

_____

_____

_____

_____

_____

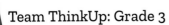

CHECK MY THINKING

1. Read the poem, "Something Told the Wild Geese" by Rachel Field.

2. Highlight one stanza of the poem that is meaningful to you. Explain your choice.

_____

_____

_____

3. Read the highlighted stanza to a partner. Ask your partner what the stanza means. After listening, share what the stanza means to you.

4. What did you learn from your partner?

_____

_____

_____

SELF-ASSESSMENT Collaborate

Collaborate – I work with others to achieve better outcomes.

Think about what you have learned about the critical thinking trait *collaborate*.

Read the sentences. Circle your answer.

4	3	2	1
I always listen to, share with, and support the work of the group.	I often listen to, share with, and support the work of the group.	I sometimes listen to, share with, and support the work of the group.	I do not listen to, share with, and support the work of the group.

Something Told the Wild Geese
by Rachel Field

Something told the wild geese
    It was time to go,
Though the fields lay golden
    Something whispered, "snow."

Leaves were green and stirring,
    Berries, luster-glossed,
But beneath warm feathers
    Something cautioned, "frost."

All the sagging orchards
    Steamed with amber spice,
But each wild breast stiffened
    At remembered ice.

Something told the wild geese
    It was time to fly,
Summer sun was on their wings,
    Winter in their cry.

Remembered for His Words

Dr. Martin Luther King Jr. was one of the greatest speakers in American history. He had the ability to communicate with all people. What made Dr. King's words so powerful?

During the time when Dr. King was a leader, life was difficult for African American people. They were not treated fairly. Dr. King wanted to encourage African Americans to carry on.

Dr. King chose words that were inspiring. His messages were positive and hopeful. He wanted his audiences to believe that they could make a difference. Dr. King asked them to imagine a better life for themselves and for others.

Dr. King wanted people to think about his words.

He used language that allowed listeners to form pictures in their minds.

For example, Dr. King once said in a speech, "Only when it is dark enough can you see the stars." These words were important to his audience. Dr. King's message was that even when times are difficult, people can still experience hope.

Dr. Martin Luther King Jr. is remembered for his words. His powerful messages continue to inspire people today.

EXPLORE THE TRAIT:

Communicate — I use clear language to express my ideas and to share information.

What techniques made Dr. Martin Luther King Jr. a powerful communicator?

_____

Imagine you traveled back in time to interview Dr. Martin Luther King Jr. Write three questions to ask Dr. King.

1. _____

2. _____

3. _____

Think about what you might like to communicate about Dr. King to others. Write a newspaper article to convey your message.

The School News Times

Volume 1, Issue 1	By the students, for the students.	Since 1978

_____

_____

_____

_____

A **found poem** is a poem created using words you *find* in a text.

Reread "Remembered for His Words." Circle or highlight words that describe the critical thinking trait *communicate.*

Read aloud your chosen words, and draw lines to connect words that fit together.

Arrange your chosen words to write a found poem. Create a title for your poem.

is given intensity
distinctive style and rhythm;
poems collectively or as a genre
of literature.

Found Poetry is a type of poetry created by taking words, phrases, and sometimes whole passages from other sources and reframing them as poetry.

Martin Luther King Jr. said, "Only when it is dark enough can you see the stars."

Other civil rights leaders communicated messages with the stars.

Harriet Tubman used the North Star as a compass as she led hundreds of people to freedom through the Underground Railroad.

The Big Dipper is an asterism, a small cluster of stars that are part of a larger constellation. The pointer stars in the Big Dipper can be used to find Polaris, the North Star.

Connect dots to design an original constellation. Write a brief narrative to communicate the legend of the constellation.

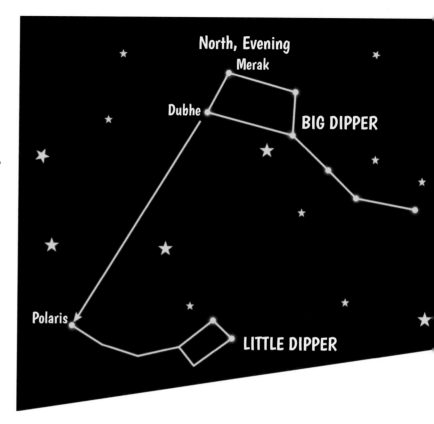

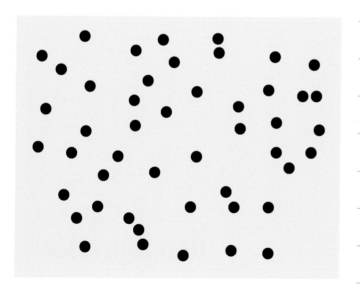

Dr. Martin Luther King Jr. chose words carefully to communicate his message. Words should also be chosen carefully to communicate math ideas. For example, instead of using the word *corner* to describe where two sides meet in a figure, mathematicians use the word *vertex*.

The words *numerator* and *denominator* are often confused. **In the graphic organizer, use words, numbers, and pictures to communicate the meanings of these words.**

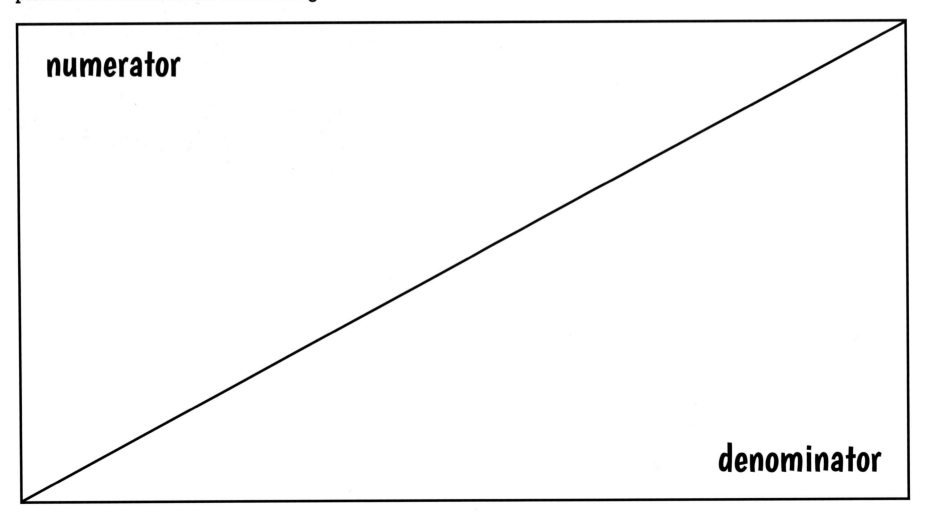

numerator

denominator

Billboards are signs used to convey important messages with images and a few words. People traveling in cars pass billboards quickly. Information on a billboard must be communicated in a simple way.

Design a billboard to communicate a message about an important cause.

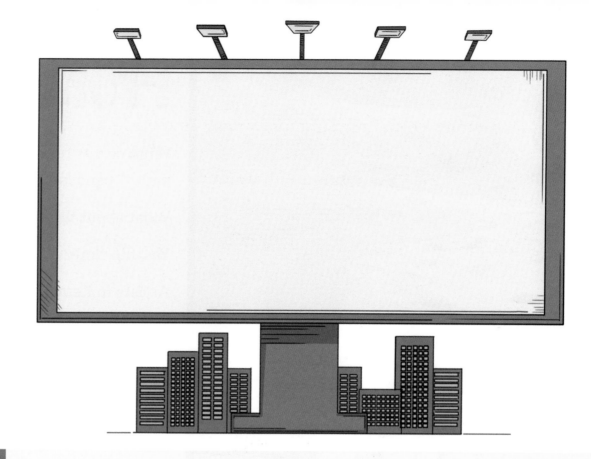

SELF-ASSESSMENT Communicate

Communicate – I use clear language to express my ideas and to share information.

Think about what you have learned about the critical thinking trait *communicate*.

Read the sentences. Color your answer.

It is easy to communicate in ways that others understand.

It is sometimes hard to communicate in ways that others understand.

I need help to communicate in ways that others understand.

From Litter to Art

What comes to mind when you think of art supplies—paint? paper? pencils?

What about flip-flops?

Yes, flip-flops!

Artists in Kenya have been using recycled flip-flops to make statues, toys, beads, and even curtains!

But why?

It started with a woman named Julie Church. She noticed many flip-flops on the beaches in Kenya. Some were left behind by people, and others washed ashore. The thousands of unwanted flip-flops destroyed the beauty of the beaches. The litter also created problems for sea animals in the water and on the beach.

Julie saw children making toys out of the discarded flip-flops. This gave her the idea to start a company called Ocean Sole®. Ocean Sole collects, washes, and cuts the old flip-flops to create beautiful new products. The work of the flip-flop artists is now sold and enjoyed in many countries.

Thanks to the flip-flop artists, the beaches in Kenya are cleaner today.

People around the world also have unique works of art to enjoy.

EXPLORE THE TRAIT:

Create — I use my knowledge and imagination to express new and innovative ideas.

Reread "From Litter to Art."

How might people benefit from Julie Church's ability to create something new?

Think about a time when you created something. Design slides to show the steps you used to create the object.

Reread "From Litter to Art."

Four footprints are left behind by the flip-flops. **Summarize the text by writing the four most important events in order on the writing lines.**

_____

_____

_____

_____

_____

_____

_____

_____

Many useful items are often thrown away. Julie Church used her imagination to create new treasures from trash.

Think of a way to create something new using each item. Draw and label your ideas.

Used tire	Empty food can	Newspaper

When you create, you use your knowledge and imagination to make something original.

In the text, you learned that ocean litter causes problems for sea animals.

Add details to the shapes in the aquarium to create sea creatures.

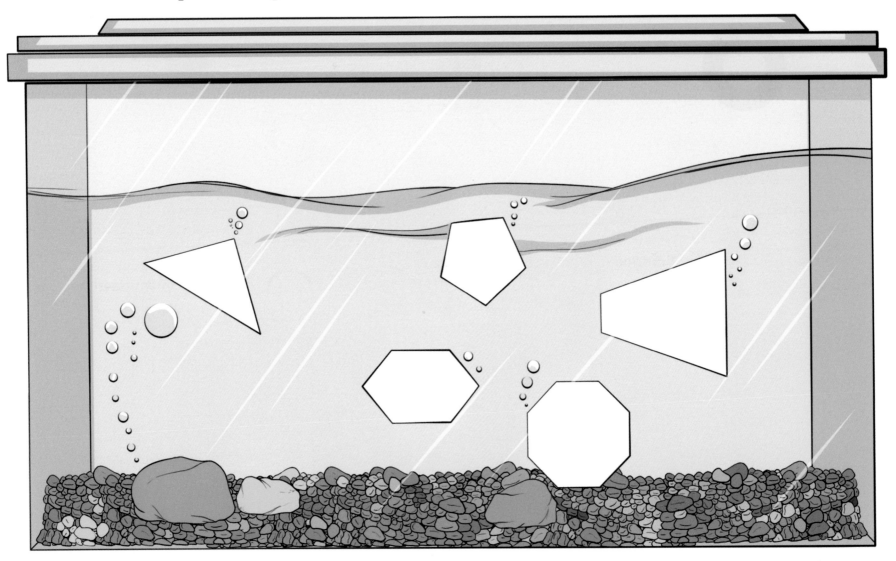

The table shows examples of famous people who created new and innovative ideas for literature, science, and math.

Famous Person	New and Innovative Idea
Dr. Seuss	wrote creative books to help children learn to read
Hans Lippershey	invented the telescope
Blaise Pascal	invented the mechanical calculator

In the chart, draw pictures to show ways you create new ideas in ELA, science, and math.

ELA	Science	Math

Create – I use my knowledge and imagination to express new and innovative ideas.

Think about what you have learned about the critical thinking trait *create*.

Read the sentences. Color your answer.

 I always create without help.

 I create most of the time with little help.

 I create, but I need help most of the time.

 I create, but I need help all the time.

 I do not create or ask for help.

The Old Lion and the Fox

an Aesop fable

There once was an old lion whose claws were worn. It was not easy for him to catch food. The old lion decided to tell his neighbors that he was sick.

Lion lay in his cave waiting for visitors. As neighbors came, he ate them one by one.

Fox came to visit Lion. But he was more distrustful of the lion than the other animals. Fox approached the cave, staying a safe distance away. "How are you feeling today, Lion?" Fox called.

"Oh, not well at all," Lion replied. "Won't you come inside?"

Fox looked closely at the footprints outside the cave. "Thank you kindly for the invitation," he said.

"But I noticed that there are many footprints leading into your cave and none coming out."

EXPLORE THE TRAIT:

Examine – I use a variety of methods to explore and to analyze.

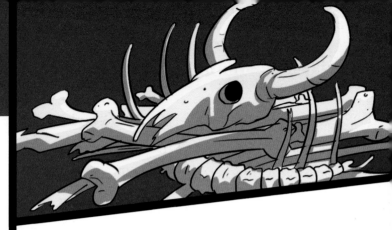

How did Fox use evidence to avoid being eaten by Lion?

_____

_____

_____

Create a superhero to help you remember the meaning of the critical thinking trait *examine*.

Name of superhero: _____

What powers does the superhero possess? _____

_____

_____

Explain how this superhero is a symbol for the meaning of the critical thinking trait *examine*. _____

_____

_____

_____

Draw a picture of your superhero.

When you read a literary text, you look closely at the plot events. You examine how one event leads to another. That strategy helps you analyze the text and better understand the meaning of the story.

Complete the graphic organizer by adding plot events to retell the fable and show how the events are connected.

which causes

which causes

which causes

which causes

which causes

How does the graphic organizer help you examine the plot of the fable?

Fox examined animal prints leading to the cave. Forensic scientists examine fingerprints.

Follow the procedure to collect and analyze your fingerprint data.

1. Use a pencil to heavily shade the empty boxes.
2. Choose your right or left hand. Rub your thumb across the first shaded box.
3. Place a piece of clear tape across your darkened thumb.
4. Remove the tape and stick it on the thumb box.
5. Use the remaining shaded boxes to capture prints from your other fingers.
6. Compare your fingerprints to the common fingerprint patterns. Then analyze the results.

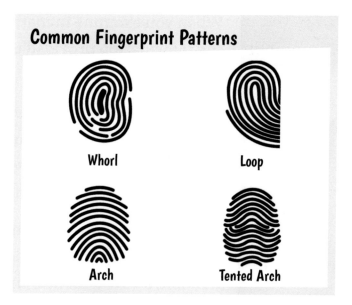

Common Fingerprint Patterns

Whorl   Loop

Arch   Tented Arch

Thumb	Pointer finger	Middle finger	Ring finger	Pinky

My fingerprint analysis

Thumb	Pointer finger	Middle finger	Ring finger	Pinky
☐ whorl	☐ whorl	☐ whorl	☐ whorl	☐ whorl
☐ loop	☐ loop	☐ loop	☐ loop	☐ loop
☐ arch	☐ arch	☐ arch	☐ arch	☐ arch
☐ tented arch	☐ tented arch	☐ tented arch	☐ tented arch	☐ tented arch

When you examine in math, you analyze the information provided to solve a problem.

In the text, Fox noticed footprints leading into Lion's cave, but no footprints coming out. By analyzing what he saw, Fox was able to draw a logical conclusion.

In the addition problem, the numbers are represented by animal heads, including a rabbit, a cow, a mouse, and a lamb. **Analyze the positions of the animal heads.** Each different head represents a different digit from 0 to 9. The same head represents the same digit. For example, all rabbits represent the same digit. **Analyze the information in the graphic to determine which digit belongs in each addition problem.**

Hint: The mouse represents 3.

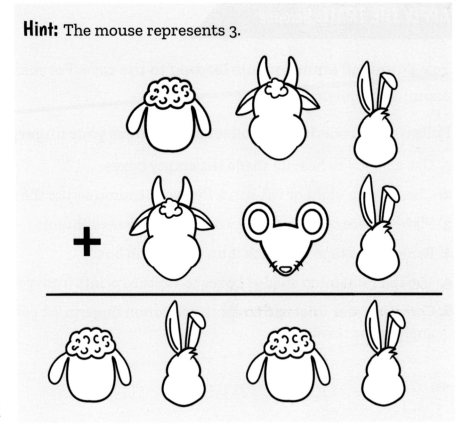

Explain how you found your answer.

_____

_____

_____

_____

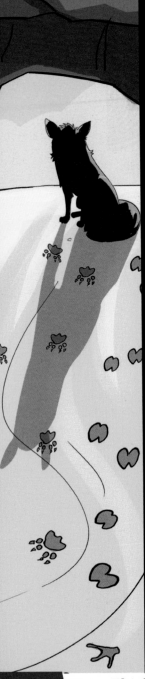

People examine their environments.

Food critics examine food.

Detectives examine clues.

Teachers examine student work.

People who examine use a variety of methods to explore and to analyze.

Read each letter. For each letter, write methods you might use to examine.

E
X
A
M
I
N
E

SELF-ASSESSMENT Examine

Examine – I use a variety of methods to explore and to analyze.

Think about what you have learned about the critical thinking trait _examine_.

Read the sentences. Circle your answer.

When I examine, I use a variety of methods to explore and to analyze.

When I examine, I use one method to explore and to analyze.

When I examine, I do not use methods to explore or to analyze.

Rocketing to Success

In 1957, Homer Hickam was 14 years old. He saw the first satellite orbit Earth while watching his family television. Homer was amazed as the Sputnik satellite flew through the sky. This event began Homer's love of rockets.

Homer grew up in a town where most people worked in the coal mines. No one knew how to build rockets. But Homer wanted to build rockets. So, he and five of his friends taught themselves about rocketry.

For the next three years, the boys studied, experimented, failed, and succeeded at launches. They learned new ways to construct and fuel the rockets. In the end, 35 of the boys' rockets took flight.

At first, Homer thought building rockets would be fun. But soon the fun was mixed with his desire to learn all he could about rockets. He said,

"I did it because I realized that I had a need to learn things."

Homer's curiosity and need to learn prepared him for service in the United States Army. He also designed spacecraft and trained astronauts at NASA.

All of this happened because of what Homer saw on television. He wanted to know if he could make rockets fly too. The answer was yes with experimentation and learning.

EXPLORE THE TRAIT:

Inquire — I seek information that excites my curiosity and inspires my learning.

How does Homer Hickam exhibit the *inquire* trait?

_____

Complete the information to launch your thinking.

3 topics you are curious about

_____

_____

_____

2 people who inspire you

_____

_____

_____

1 question you wonder about

_____

_____

_____

Blast off!

When you apply the *inquire* trait, you think of questions that will help you locate information you are curious about. These questions will also encourage you to learn more.

When you research a topic, you think about what you already know about the topic. Then you think about what you would like to learn about the topic. The focus of your research should be on what you want to learn. You guide your research by writing strong questions. **Practice writing strong questions on this graphic organizer.**

Write a topic on the open book.

Then write questions in the *Who? What? Where? When? Why? How?* thought bubbles that will help you learn more about the topic.

Homer Hickam loved rockets. **Learn about one way to construct rockets.**

Straw Rocket

Materials: drinking straw, paper, tape, scissors, ruler, pencil

Instructions:

1. Cut across the top of a sheet of paper to make a strip 8 ½ inches long and 2 inches wide.

2. Roll the paper around a pencil to make a cylinder, and secure it with tape.

3. Remove the paper cylinder from the pencil.

4. Cut more paper to make fins and a nose cone.

5. Tape the fins and nose cone to the cylinder.

6. Place the rocket over the straw, and launch by blowing into the straw.

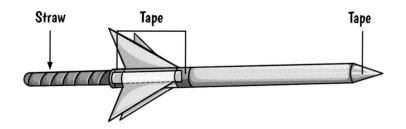

Straw   Tape   Tape

Imagine you want to test the rocket. To experiment with the rocket, you might change the length of the straw, the fins, or the nose cone.

What might you change if you were experimenting with the straw rocket?

_____

_____

_____

How does your rocket compare to rockets that travel in space?

_____

_____

_____

What else do you wonder about rockets?

_____

_____

_____

When you inquire in mathematics, you ask questions and seek information that satisfies your curiosity.

In the text, Homer Hickam and his friends were curious about rockets. Their curiosity led them to learn many things about rocketry. Today, model rocketry is a popular hobby. Many adults and children join rocket clubs to learn more about rocketry.

This table provides information about five different model rocket kits. It tells the mass of each rocket in grams, the possible altitude each rocket may reach in feet, and the cost of the kit in dollars.

Use the table to determine a question that might result in each answer.

Model Rockets

Rocket Name	Mass (grams)	Altitude (feet)	Cost ($)
Red Rover	68	600	18
Blue Blaze	79	545	15
Sky King	43	1,100	12
Screaming Eagle	71	575	17
Quick Silver	18	1,600	13

1. The answer is 500 feet. What might be the question?

_____

_____

2. The answer is 25 grams. What might be the question?

_____

_____

3. The answer is $44. What might be the question?

_____

_____

4. The answer is Blue Blaze. What might be the question?

_____

_____

5. Now, it is your turn to write an answer. Then have a partner write a question that might result in that answer.

The answer is: _____

_____

The question might be: _____

_____

A glyph is a design that communicates information without using words.

Follow the directions to create a personal rocket glyph of your interests.

1. If you like working by yourself, color the nose cone red.

   If you like working with a group, color the nose cone yellow.

2. If math is your favorite subject, color the body tube blue.

   If reading is your favorite subject, color the body tube purple.

   If science is your favorite subject, color the body tube green.

3. If you like playing outside, color the window orange.

   If you like playing inside, color the window yellow.

4. If you like to draw, color the tail fins black.

   If you do not like to draw, color the tail fins brown.

5. If you like to read fiction books, color the flames orange.

   If you like to read nonfiction books, color the flames red.

6. If you have a hobby, add stars to the sky.

SELF-ASSESSMENT Inquire

Inquire – I seek information that excites my curiosity and inspires my learning.

Think about what you have learned about the critical thinking trait *inquire*.

- Color three question marks if you always inquire.
- Color two question marks if you inquire most of the time.
- Color one question mark if you inquire, but you need help.
- Do not color any question marks if you do not inquire.

Draw to Remember

Your teacher shares a lot of new information with you each day. When you read, you learn even more ideas.

What if you have many things to complete after school? Sometimes, it might seem like too much to remember. What's a brain to do?

Scientists say, "Draw!"

Scientists tried this idea in a study. They gave two groups of people long lists of words to remember. One group tried to remember the words by writing them many times. The second group drew pictures to represent the words.

Then the scientists tested both groups of people. The scientists wanted to see how many words each group remembered.

The group that drew pictures of the words remembered almost twice as many words as the group who wrote them!

What if you're not a great artist? Don't worry. Scientists say your drawing skills don't matter.

It is the process of drawing that helps you recall ideas later.

Try this strategy the next time your brain has a lot to remember!

Link – I apply knowledge to reach new understandings.

How do drawings help people link and connect information?

Drawings are visual representations. **Draw visual representations for the words in the link trait definition. Then provide an association for the words.**

apply		reach	
Visual representation	Association *This word reminds me of …*	Visual representation	Association *This word reminds me of …*
knowledge		**understandings**	
Visual representation	Association *This word reminds me of …*	Visual representation	Association *This word reminds me of …*

When you link your thinking, you apply what you know to learn and to create something new.

Words are organized in groups by the way they are used in sentences. These groups are called *parts of speech*.

Read the descriptions of nouns, verbs, adjectives, and adverbs. Then list words that belong in each group. Finally, draw a symbol that will help you remember these parts of speech.

Nouns name people, places, things, and ideas.	Verbs name actions.	Adjectives describe people, places, things, or ideas.	Adverbs describe how, when, and where actions are done.
Symbol	Symbol	Symbol	Symbol

Scientists and engineers use drawings in many ways.

They use drawings to record detailed observations, to plan new inventions, and to sketch ideas they want to remember.

The drawings help scientists and engineers link knowledge to make new connections.

Review different types of drawings used by scientists and engineers.

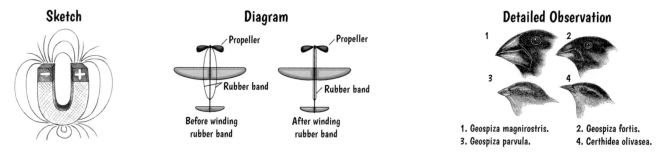

Complete different types of drawings in the spaces below.

Sketch a solid object.	Diagram the life cycle of an insect.	Draw detailed observations of your thumb.	Create a blueprint for an invention.

How might you use the drawings to link ideas?

When you link in math, you use what you know to connect ideas.

Scientists found that drawing pictures often helps students remember the meanings of words. In mathematics, drawing pictures often helps students solve problems. **Draw a picture to help solve the problem.**

There are 5 children in a line to purchase tickets for the movie. John is before Smith in the line, but they are not standing next to each other. Maria and Terri always stand next to each other. Olive is last in line. Smith is directly behind Terri. In what order are the children in line?

Turn to a partner, and compare your solutions. Explain how your picture supports your answer.

Write a word in each puzzle piece that relates to the puzzle pieces connected to it.

An example is done for you.

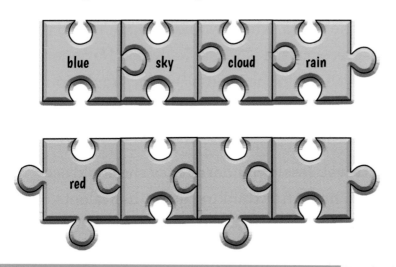

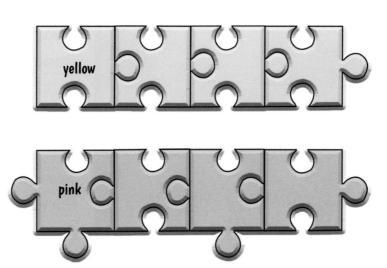

SELF-ASSESSMENT Link

Link – I apply knowledge to reach new understandings.

Think about what you have learned about the critical thinking trait *link*.

Read the sentences. Circle your answer.

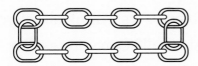

I always apply knowledge to
reach new understandings.

I often apply knowledge to
reach new understandings.

I never apply knowledge to
reach new understandings.

Willing to Volunteer, Willing to Travel

If you could travel anywhere in the world, where would you go? Would you stand beneath one of the tallest trees in the world in Redwood National Park? Would you snorkel with sea lions in the Pacific Ocean? Would you take a selfie with the Queen's Guard at Buckingham Palace? Jessie Festa can show you how.

Jessie is a writer. She loves to travel. Jessie wondered how she could see the world and still earn money to live. After thinking about her talents, Jessie decided to write a travel blog.

Jessie's blog tells the stories of her travel adventures.

Her stories describe her thoughts and experiences during her travels.

Many of her trips involve volunteering in interesting places. When she writes about helping others, she thinks about how she might help other people in other places.

Jessie offers these suggestions to traveling volunteers. First, think about your skills. Can you read a book to a person who is lonely or ill? Can you teach a game or sport to a younger child? Can you paint a fence or weed a garden?

Next, look for opportunities to use your skills in places you would like to visit. Think about working with local organizations that help people. Soon, you will be off on fantastic adventures, helping others and seeing the world.

EXPLORE THE TRAIT:

Reflect – I review my thoughts and experiences to guide my actions.

How does Jessie use the **reflect** trait when she blogs about her travels?

_____

Think about the words in the *reflect* trait definition. Check the statement that describes your knowledge of each word. Explain what you think each word means.

Word	My knowledge of the word	What I think the word means
review	☐ This word is new to me. ☐ I think I know the meaning. ☐ I know the meaning.	
thoughts	☐ This word is new to me. ☐ I think I know the meaning. ☐ I know the meaning.	
experiences	☐ This word is new to me. ☐ I think I know the meaning. ☐ I know the meaning.	
guide	☐ This word is new to me. ☐ I think I know the meaning. ☐ I know the meaning.	
actions	☐ This word is new to me. ☐ I think I know the meaning. ☐ I know the meaning.	

In "Willing to Volunteer, Willing to Travel," Jessie recommends asking these questions if you want to volunteer.

- Can you read a book to a person who is lonely or ill?
- Can you teach a game or sport to a younger child?
- Can you paint a fence or weed a garden?

Imagine that you complete a volunteer activity.

Plan a postcard that you would send to a family member or friend to tell about your experience. On the front of your postcard, sketch an image that shows you in action. On the back of the postcard, write a short description of your experience and what you learned from volunteering.

FRONT	BACK
Sketch	Description

Name

Address

City, State, ZIP

Jessie Festa travels around the world.

Imagine that you could travel to another world. Which planet would you like to visit?

Use these steps to complete the graphic organizer about the planet you chose.

1. Write what you know about the planet you would like to visit in the *K* column.
2. Record information you want to know about the planet in the *W* column.
3. Use reference materials to learn more about the planet. Record the information you learn in the *L* column.

K	W	L
What I know about the planet	What I want to know about the planet	What I learned about the planet

Travel brochures provide travelers with information about destinations. **Use the information discovered about your chosen planet to make a travel brochure that encourages people to visit the planet.**

Create the travel brochure on the provided paper.

When you reflect in math, you think about what you know and use the information to solve a problem.

Jessie traveled to many different points on the globe. **Use your knowledge of multiples and the points on the circle to create a design.**

Follow these directions.

- Place your pencil on the point for the number 6.

- Use a ruler to draw a line from 6 to the next multiple of 6.

- Then draw lines from 6 to the remaining multiples of 6 found on the circle.

- Place your pencil on the point for the number 12.

- Draw lines from 12 to the remaining multiples of 6 found on the circle.

- Continue this process to draw lines from the remaining multiples of 6 to all the other multiples of 6.

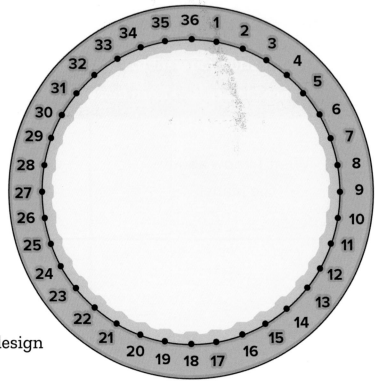

Reflection Questions

What polygon was outlined when the large group completed the design for multiples of 9?

How does this reflect the relationship between 9 and 36?

What polygon was outlined when you completed the design for multiples of 6?

How does this reflect the relationship between 6 and 36?

What polygon do you predict will be outlined if you complete a design showing multiples of 4?

Travelers use maps to help them reach destinations. People set goals and make plans to help them reach goals.

Set a goal for yourself. Then make a plan to reach the goal.

As you work to meet your goal, reflect about parts of the plan that are successful and what you might need to improve.

To reach my goal, I will:

To track my progress, I will:

My goal is:

Reflect – I review my thoughts and experiences to guide my actions.

Think about what you have learned about the critical thinking trait *reflect*.

Read the sentences. Check your answer.

☐ I reflect without being told to do so.

☐ I reflect but only after being told to do so.

☐ I reflect most of the time without being told to do so.

☐ I do not reflect.

In It to Win It

On July 5th, 2015, more than 25 million people across the United States watched a soccer match.

But it wasn't just any soccer match. It was the Women's World Cup.

The World Cup is played every four years. The U.S. women's national team had lost the tournament in 2011. They were determined to win in 2015.

For four years, the players practiced long hours. They exercised and ate healthy foods. Their coaches planned new plays. The team members worked together to improve their skills. They knew that if they stayed focused on their goal, they would win.

That is exactly what happened. The team defeated six teams in the tournament to play in the final match. They defeated the team from Japan by a score of 5 to 2.

The U.S. women's national team achieved its goal—a World Cup victory.

Strive — I use effort and determination to focus on challenging tasks.

What did the players on the U.S. women's national team learn from their World Cup loss in 2011?

Coaches often give short speeches called pep talks to encourage their teams.

List several goals in the space between the ball and the net. Circle the goal that you think will be the most challenging.

Write a pep talk to yourself to strive to meet your goals.

When you strive, you stay focused on your goal and give effort and determination to accomplish it.

Read this quote by Sydney Leroux, a member of the U.S. women's national team in 2015.

"I worked on my weaknesses and made them my strengths."

Use the graphic organizer to plan a personal narrative based on this quote.

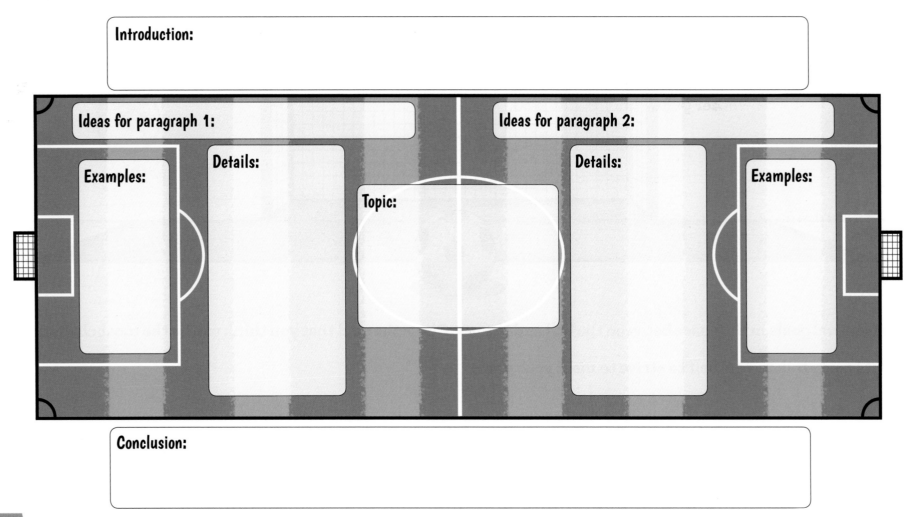

Introduction:

Ideas for paragraph 1:

Examples:

Details:

Topic:

Ideas for paragraph 2:

Details:

Examples:

Conclusion:

An unbalanced force is a push or pull that causes an object to move, stop, or change direction.

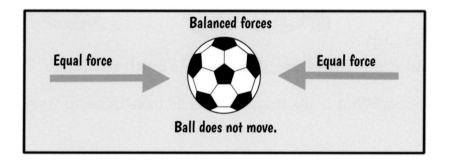

Balanced forces

Equal force → ← Equal force

Ball does not move.

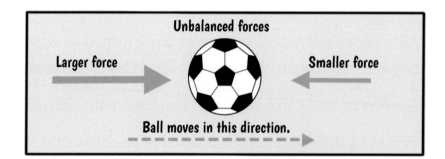

Unbalanced forces

Larger force → ← Smaller force

Ball moves in this direction.

Demonstrate and observe how position and motion can be changed by forces in a paper soccer game.

Trace the finger puppet on provided paper.

Make a soccer ball and soccer goals out of paper.

Play finger puppet soccer against a classmate.

Record observations. Draw arrows to show the direction that force is applied and the motion of the ball.

5

Finger puppet pattern

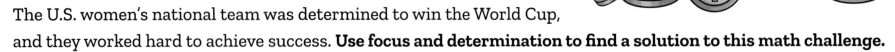

When you strive in math, you focus on a problem and look for ways to find a solution.

The U.S. women's national team was determined to win the World Cup, and they worked hard to achieve success. **Use focus and determination to find a solution to this math challenge.**

Mrs. Lee has 14 coins in her purse. The total value of her coins is 86¢. What coins might Mrs. Lee have in her purse?

Find at least 3 different combinations of 14 coins that total 86¢.

_____

_____

Explain a strategy you used to solve this problem.

_____

_____

Were you able to use a mistake to help find a correct solution? _____

Explain your answer.

_____

_____

CHECK MY THINKING

After the U.S. women's national team won the World Cup in 2015, New York City honored them with a ticker tape parade. The first ticker tape parade was held in 1886 to honor the Statue of Liberty. New York City has hosted more than 200 ticker tape parades to celebrate military victories and to honor presidents, sports stars, and astronauts.

Think of goals you have strived to accomplish this year.

Imagine you are being honored with a parade for one of the goals you met.

Describe the goal and how you used the *strive* trait to reach the goal.

_____

_____

_____

SELF-ASSESSMENT Strive

***Strive* – I use effort and determination to focus on challenging tasks.**

Think about what you have learned about the critical thinking trait *strive*.

Read the sentences. Circle your answer.

I always focus on challenging tasks.

I often need help with challenging tasks.

I give up before finishing challenging tasks.

Notes

Notes

Reflections

1002330 | April 2019 | Four Color Press | Ft. Worth, Texas